When We
Were Young

THE 1960s

When We
Were Young
THE 1960s

Tony Husband

ARCTURUS

ARCTURUS

This edition published in 2017 by Arcturus Publishing Limited
26/27 Bickels Yard, 151–153 Bermondsey Street,
London SE1 3HA

Copyright © Arcturus Holdings Limited/Tony Husband

ISBN: 978-1-78428-696-5
AD005575UK

Printed in Italy

Contents

Decade of Change

The Britain of the early Sixties was a world away from the one we know today. Nothing much happened most of the time. Pubs and shops had restricted hours. TV was in black and white and there were only two channels. But then came a revolution in fashion, humour and pop music, and everything went psychedelic ...

If the 1950s were in black and white,
the 1960s were in colour.

Old Father Time felt young again.

'Typical, I lived through the hardships of the
Forties, the boring Fifties and now I'm too old to
enjoy the Sixties.'

'He's just seen his first mini skirt.'

'They're dead posh them – they have an inside toilet.'

'Yuri Gagarin will be passing by in his space ship soon,
get ready to wave.'

'Mum, the Fifties won't come back, will they?'

'Maybe we'll not stay over at that new motel after all;
let's head straight home.'

'No, we've not complained to our neighbours about the noise, but then we do live next door to the Kray Twins.'

'They're the Elizabeth Taylor and Richard Burton
of the White Lion.'

'She went to a Rolling Stones concert last week and
hasn't been the same since.'

'Are you sure you've been working late at the House, darling?'

'A white wine for her and a vodka dry martini for me,
shaken not stirred.'

'It's too risky. It might seem like a good price now,
but who knows how far prices could fall in
the next few decades.'

'It's a pirate radio station.'

'Dad, I told you not to kick my ball in your
winkle-pickers.'

'We don't mind you listening to your favourite music, but
you've been in there since 9 a.m.'

'Mark my words. The Cuban Missile Crisis will be the end for all of us, so you may as well know I love you, Laura.'

Mini skirts kept going up.

'I'll be thinking of Cliff on the coach to Cleethorpes
next week.'

'Some people just weren't made to wear hipsters.'

'You'd never catch me in one of those bubble cars.'

'Are you a mod or a rocker?'
'(Gulp) I'm whatever you are...'

'One day they'll make one that fits in your pocket.'

'For heaven's sake: Coronation Street! Who'd want to
watch a TV series about a grimy northern town?!
It'll never last.'

'Go to sleep or the Russians will get you.'

You were either a Beatles or a Stones fan.

Conspiracy theories were rife.
'Psst! Get me a top-up and I'll tell you who killed Kennedy!'

'The Daleks scare us too, son.'

Swinging Britain

Suburban Britain remained staunchly conservative, but for a magical couple of years London became world leader in practically everything. The rise in prosperity brought freedom and crazy fashions: unisex, velvet jackets, mini skirts, kaftans and long hair for men. The joint was swinging.

'Look, Mum, John Steed from the Avengers!'

'Hi, Josie, do you and Peter want to come over for dinner? We've had a big delivery of Vesta curries.'

'It's bad news I'm afraid, Mrs Smith. Your daughter has Beatlemania.'

'Get to the bathroom this minute. I bet Batman and
Robin brush their teeth every morning and night.'

'It was a really strange night. They burned joss sticks
and kept calling me "man".'

'I love our quiet weekends by the sea.'

'Yahoo!! With a team like this, we'll be winning World Cups
for many years to come.'

'Why couldn't you have found the World Cup instead of Pickles?'

'Joan, I've packed in my job. I'm going to turn on, tune in and drop out.'

'My husband? No, he's out... he's gone to a happening.'

'I bet that Twiggy has to run around in the shower
to get wet.'

'Hi, I'm from t'North. Where can I get some of this free love?'

'Got a mini for my birthday from my parents!'
'Car?!!' 'No, skirt.'

'Oh great, a 30-minute drum solo.'

'Daddy, I'm going to India to find myself. Can you pay?'

'Is this where you sign up for the hippy trail?'

'It seems the Sixties are passing me by.'

'The Magic Roundabout is so... heavy, man!!'

'This place is really really far out, man! But can anybody remember the way home?!'

'You stay clear of all that free love,
do you hear, Deirdre?!!'

'Perhaps we should get him some of those headphones for his birthday.'

'I'm only here because I heard there was a groovy
scene going on.'

'Yes, Grandad, I know you can play guitar with your teeth,
but that's not how Jimi Hendrix does it.'

'Rubbish... !'   'Genius... !'

'What's today's demo about?!'

'I know you want to find yourself, but how about finding a job first?'

'I don't care if Georgie Best has hair down to his shoulders, you're off to the barber's, young man.'

'She dreams of joining Pan's People.'

'It's our Barry. They're calling the baby Daffodil Moon.'

'I'll just put another penny on the needle...
it sounds much heavier then.'

'It's okay, they'll soon spot us: I'm wearing flares!'

Feeling Groovy

In the Sixties, a never-ending argument began between parents and their offspring. This was known as the 'generation gap'. But change was unrelenting. Man landed on the Moon; the Vietnam war split America; the Beatles met the Maharishi. And everything was bigger and brighter than it had ever been before.

'I've called him Jagger.'

'I'm having a bed-in like John and Yoko.'

'What will we be doing in fifty years' time? Not this,
that's for sure.'

'You're still missing life at sea, aren't you, Alec?'

'C'mon, get up... You're lucky: if you were American, you'd be in Vietnam.'

'Oh no, darling. The mini is so not in any more.
It's the maxi now.'

'They've discovered oil in the North Sea, but they're never going to be able to get it out, surely?!'

'How do you spell "ROOL"?'

'He's got your, er, hair.'

'We ate out last night. It was really posh: they had cheese and pineapple on a stick.' 'Wow!'

'If I was a rock star with a Rolls-Royce, I'd drive it into my pool... if I had a pool, that is.'

'It's our Ashley. He's been arrested outside the American embassy. He's ringing to find out if we're proud or angry.'

'That's one small step for man and one... damn, what
was it again?'

'I'm going to see Hair tonight.'

'Look, there's that bloke off the television.'

'Man's landed on the Moon and you can't even put up
a flamin' shelf.'

'Oh, I see. Now Pot Black's on our new TV, I've discovered the balls are different colours.'

'Wow, you fly Concorde.'

'I'm telling you, man: if you can remember the Sixties,
you weren't there.'